"For the Lord shall comfort Zion: he will comfort all her waste places; and he will make her wilderness like Eden, and her desert like THE GARDEN of the Lord; joy and gladness shall be found therein, thanksgiving, and the voice of melody."

(Isaiah 51:3; emphasis added)

THE GARDEN

An Allegorical Oratorio

words and music by

MICHAEL McLEAN
& BRYCE NEUBERT

based on the musical score by

MERRILL JENSON

arrangements by

GREG HANSEN & DAN WALDIS

Deseret Book Company
Salt Lake City, Utah

Graphic design: Shauna Gibby
Cover photo: Scot Proctor
Cover illustration: Greg Olsen

All songs: lyrics by Michael McLean, music by Bryce Neubert
© 1995 Shining Star Music (ASCAP) and AudioArt Creative Concepts (BMI).

Visit us at www.deseretbook.com

ISBN 1-57345-071-5

Printed in the United States of America   72076
Publishers Printing, Salt Lake City, UT

10 9 8 7 6 5

CONTENTS

INTRODUCTION

Since we cannot remember what it was like or exactly what we did before we were born, it is impossible to accurately describe what a celestial amphitheater might have looked like, if there even was such a thing. But try to imagine one. And while you're picturing some kind of heavenly performing arts center, imagine a large crowd gathering. In that heavenly air there is a feeling of both reverence and excitement, for we have come to hear a musical presentation before we all leave our spiritual home to come to an earthly one.

We have all been taught, perfectly, the purpose for our leaving the presence of our Heavenly Father and coming to earth. We understand the plan. But because everything we hope to become hinges on the events that will take place on the earth we are about to inhabit, we find that we can't talk enough, dream enough, think enough, or sing enough with each other about the adventure that awaits us. The musical presentation we are about to hear is not intended to answer all our questions about what life on earth will really be like, or how our individual lives will unfold, but, rather, it is a humble and artistic attempt by a group of musicians to focus our spiritual hearts and minds in a creatively different way on what will be the central event in all human history—the atoning sacrifice of Jesus Christ.

The stage is set. There is a choir. There is an orchestra. There are seven soloists.

Just before the performance begins, one of the authors of the work we are about to hear takes center stage to offer a few words of welcome and explanation. He seems a bit nervous.

"When you were invited to this presentation you were told this would be an ALLEGORICAL ORATORIO, and many of you have asked us what that means. Well, an oratorio, as most of you know, is a musical composition on a sacred theme for solo voices, chorus, and orchestra that is dramatic and tells a connected story. We call our creation an 'allegorical oratorio' because in an allegory the telling of the moral or religious tale is figurative or symbolic. I say this because we don't want any of you to think that our soloists, who will be singing as if they were an olive tree or a millstone or a seedling, actually believe that any of us will spend our lives on earth as these elements in a garden. In the piece you are about to hear, our soloists and chorus will be telling this story as if true, leaving you to discover its fictitious characters and learn its lesson. Thank you so much for coming and giving us this opportunity to leave our witness that no matter what trials we may face on the earth, a Savior will come to save those of us who are willing to be saved."

As the author leaves the stage, a conductor signals to the orchestra that it is time to begin.

An introduction to the performance, sung by soloists and choir: "We have come to tell a story,...and we hope...
the meaning will be heard,...that we need not be afraid."

PROLOGUE

Arranged by
GREG HANSEN

Words and Music by
BRYCE NEUBERT &
MICHAEL McLEAN

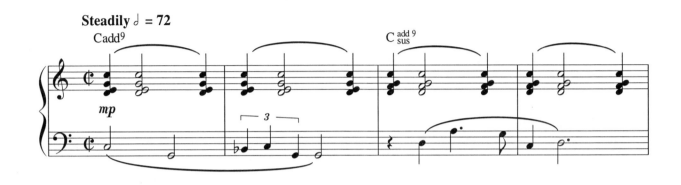

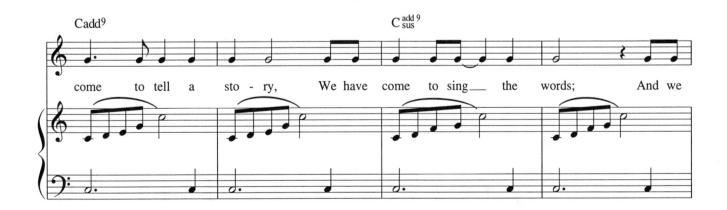

1

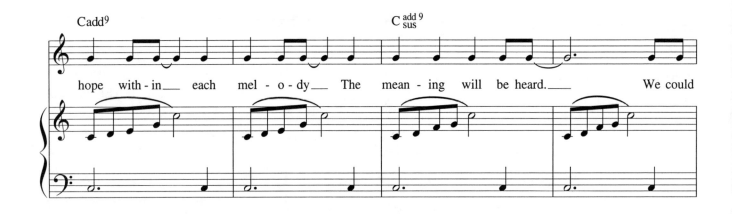

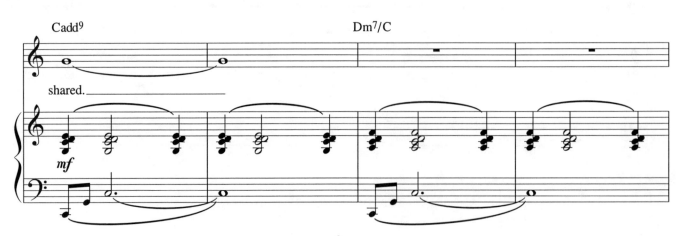

3

The setting for our allegory is a Garden. If you listen with your heart, you will hear the Garden sing.

THE GARDEN

Arranged by
GREG HANSEN

Words and Music by
BRYCE NEUBERT &
MICHAEL McLEAN

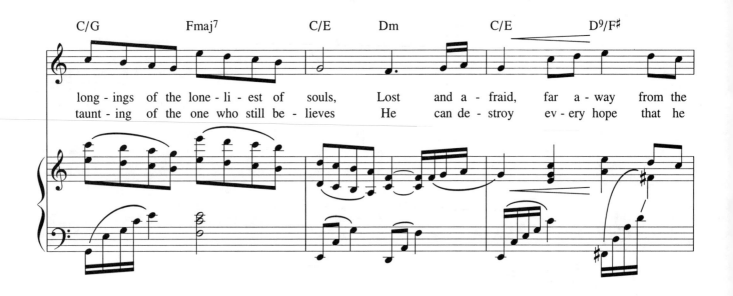

long - ings of the lone - li - est of souls, Lost and a - fraid, far a - way from the
taunt - ing of the one who still be - lieves He can de - stroy ev - ery hope that he

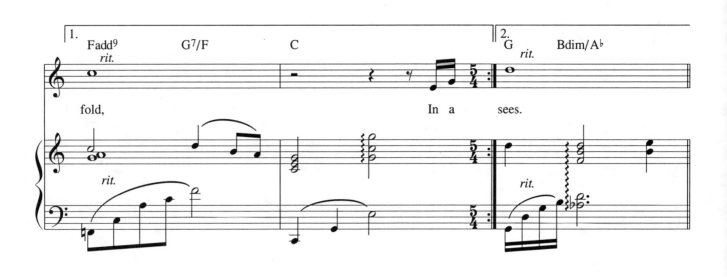

fold, In a sees.

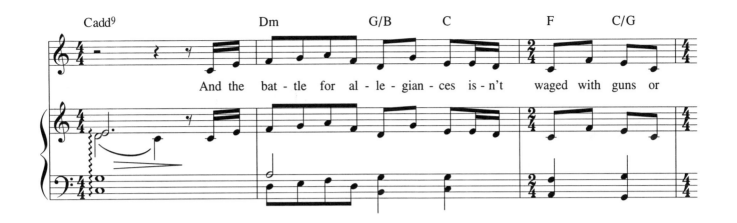

And the bat - tle for al - le - gian - ces is - n't waged with guns or

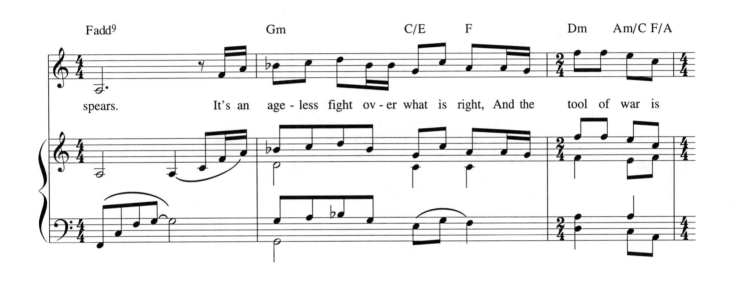

spears. It's an age - less fight ov - er what is right, And the tool of war is

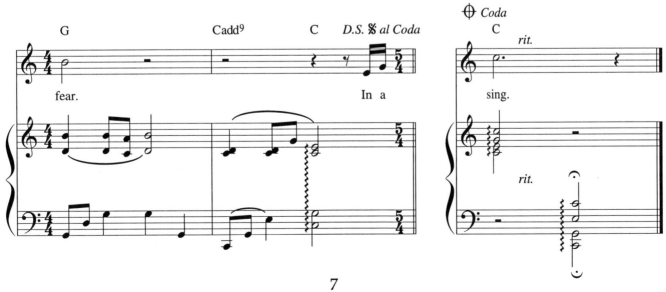

fear. In a sing.

7

A Seedling, trapped beneath the earth and unable to grow, sings plaintively of its fears and frustrations.
"Are there reasons I should know, why I can't grow?"

I CAN'T GROW
(The Seedling)

Arranged by
GREG HANSEN

Words and Music by
BRYCE NEUBERT &
MICHAEL McLEAN

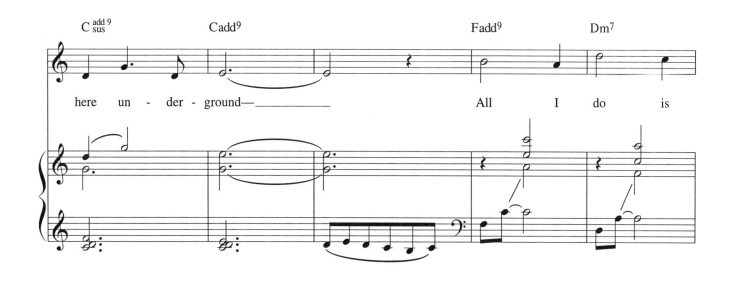

here un - der - ground—_____ All I do is

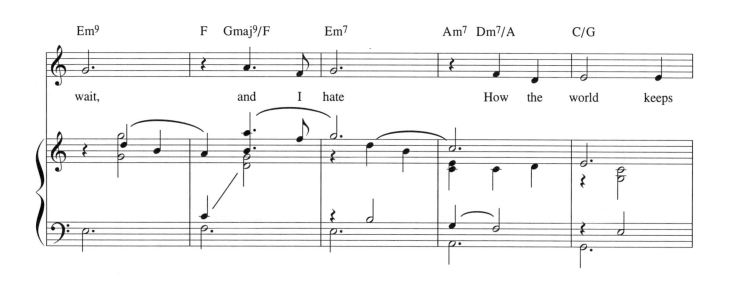

wait, and I hate How the world keeps

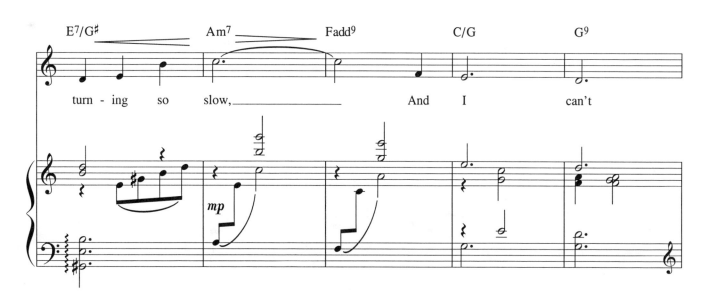

turn - ing so slow,_____ And I can't

9

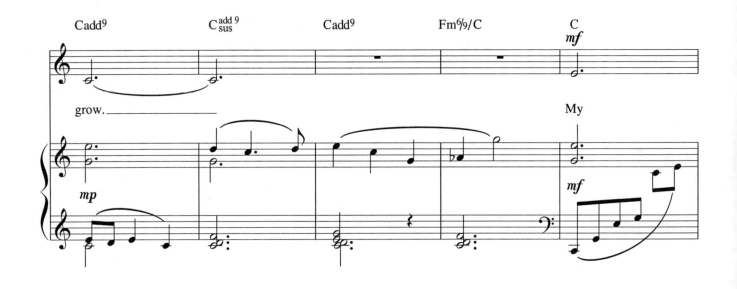

grow. _____ My

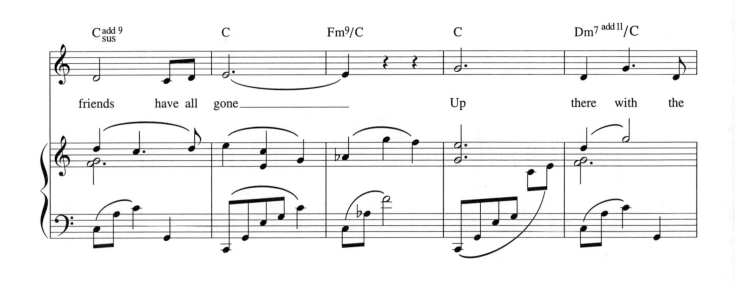

friends have all gone _____ Up there with the

sun. _____ But I've been here so long—

10

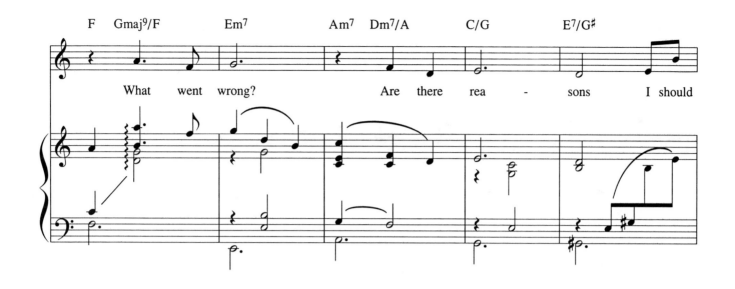

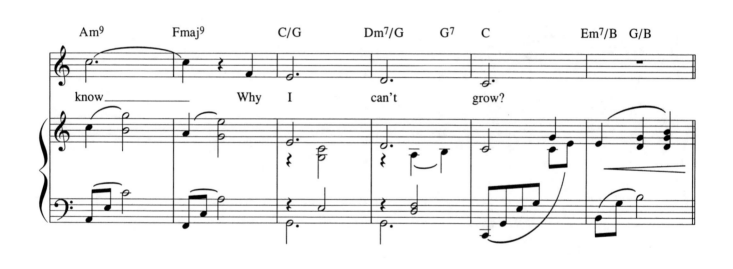

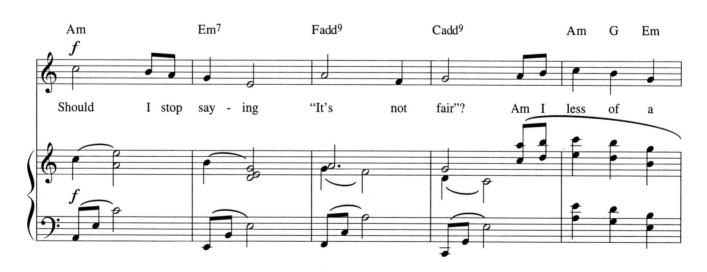

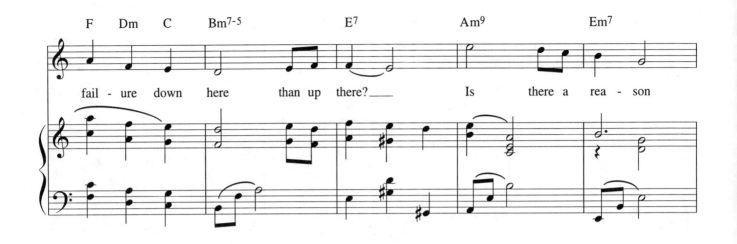

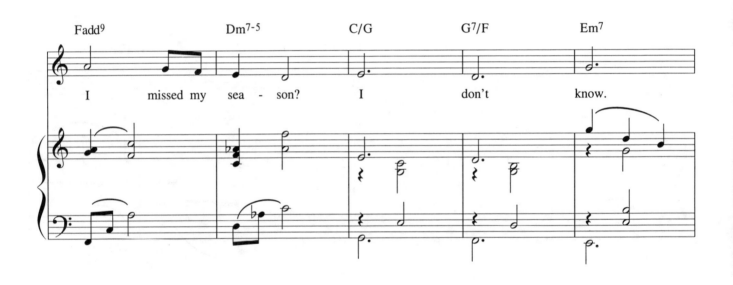

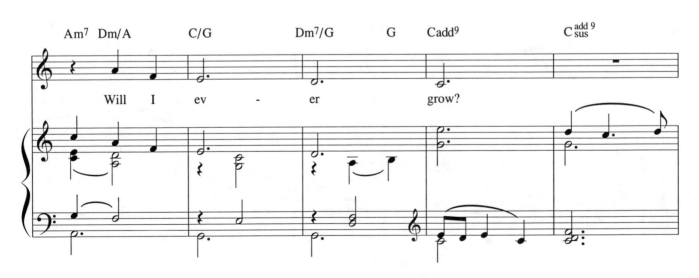

12

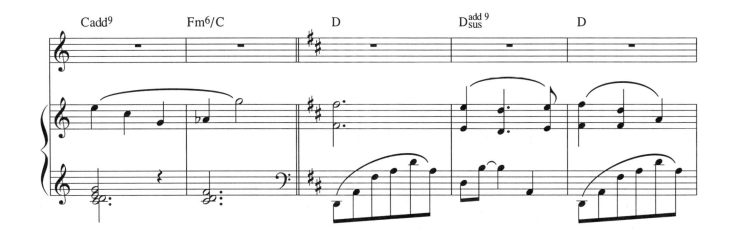

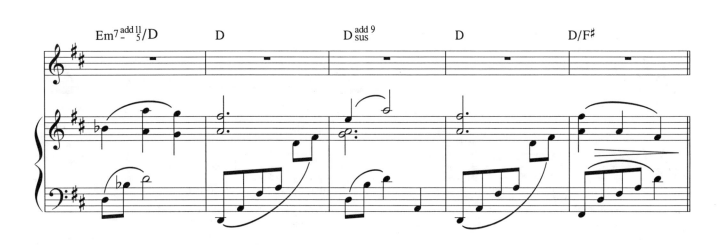

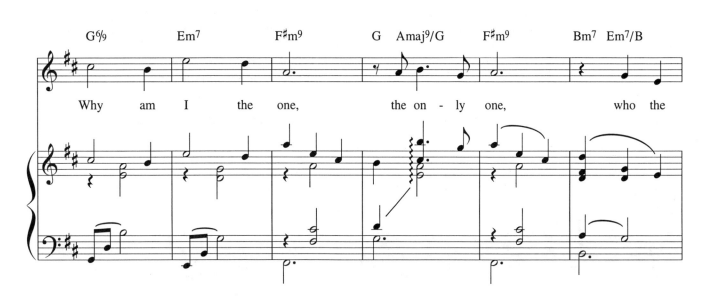

Why am I the one, the on - ly one, who the

13

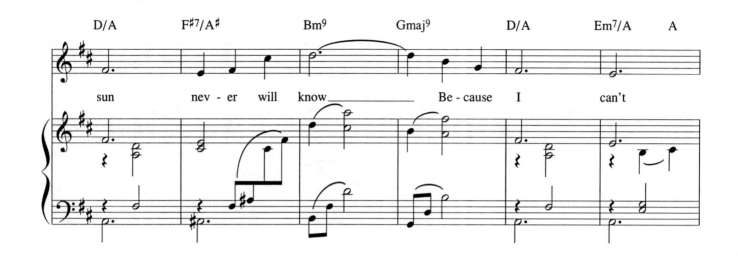

sun nev - er will know_____ Be - cause I can't

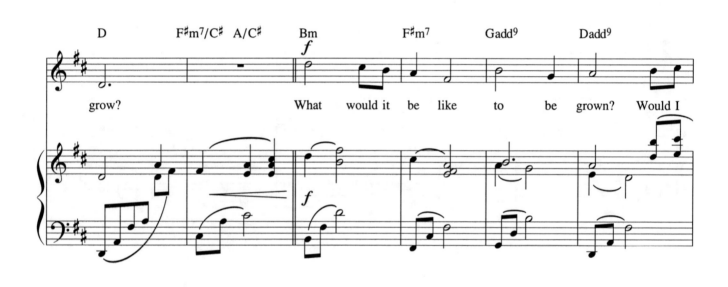

grow? What would it be like to be grown? Would I

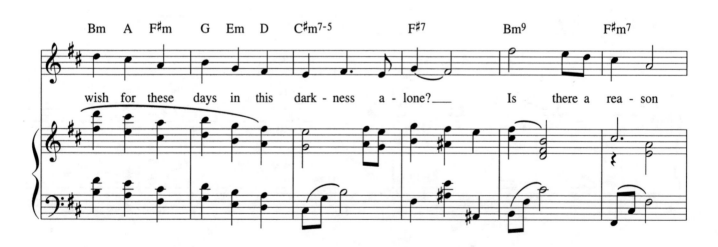

wish for these days in this dark - ness a - lone?_____ Is there a rea - son

14

I missed my sea - son? I don't know. Will I

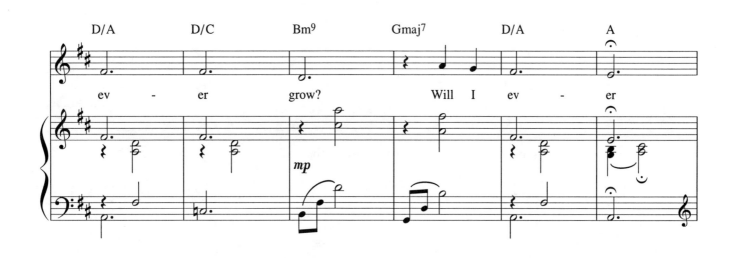

ev - er grow? Will I ev - er

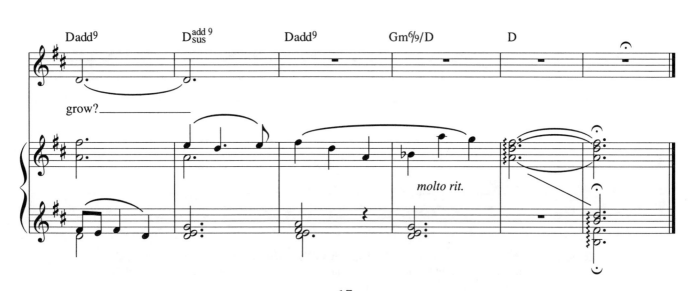

grow?_____

molto rit.

15

A Ram, caught in a nearby thicket, hears the Seedling's lament. He too is frustrated. Ensnared due to his own foolishness, he decries the mistakes he has made and vows: "The next time I'm called at the end of the day, I'll run to my shepherd's side."

NEXT TIME
(The Ram in the Thicket)

Arranged by
GREG HANSEN

Words and Music by
BRYCE NEUBERT &
MICHAEL McLEAN

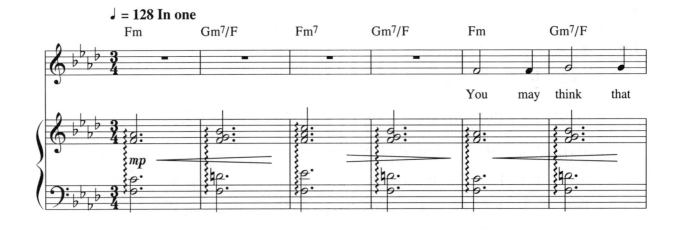

You may think that

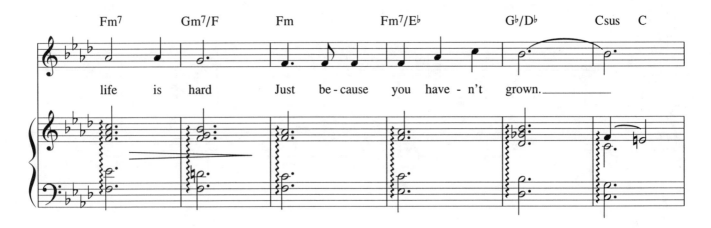

life is hard Just be-cause you have-n't grown.

You should stay right where you are; It's much hard-er up here on your

16

18

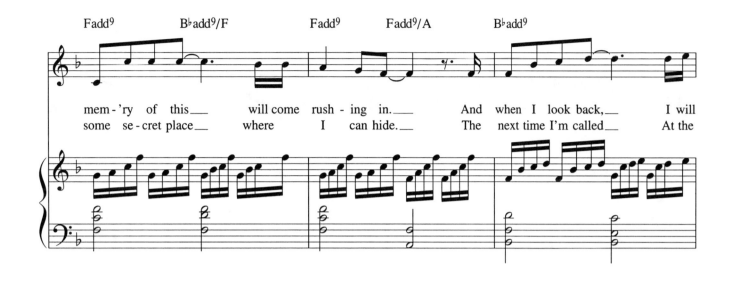

mem-'ry of this___ will come rush-ing in.___ And when I look back,___ I will
some se-cret place___ where I can hide.___ The next time I'm called___ At the

al - ways re-call___ Just how big a fool I've been.
end of the day,___ I'll run to my shep-herd's side.

Next time I won't get lost. Next time I'll see the

20

The Chorus sings about the elements in the Garden that seem to relish the growing hopelessness. The Snake and the weeds and thistles are agents of one who loves darkness rather than light.

A SNAKE LIES IN THE GRASS
(The Chorus)

Arranged by
DAN WALDIS

Words and Music by
BRYCE NEUBERT &
MICHAEL McLEAN

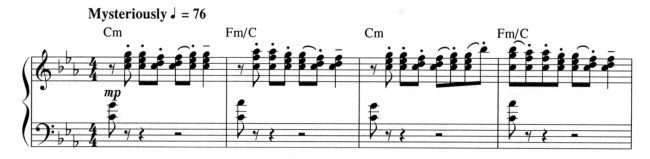

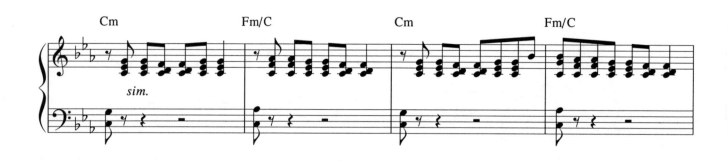

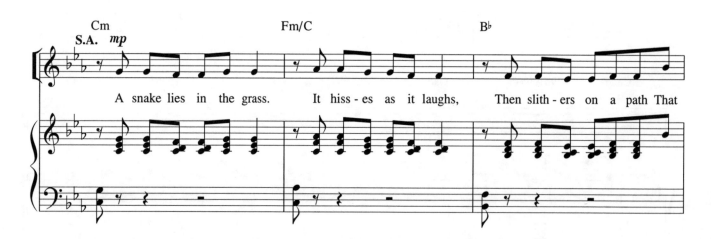

A snake lies in the grass. It hiss-es as it laughs, Then slith-ers on a path That

23

The au-thor of this sad-ness, In all his ev-il mad-ness, A-waits in twist-ed glad-ness

For the news that all the gar-den's his.

A snake lies in the grass. It hiss-es as it laughs,

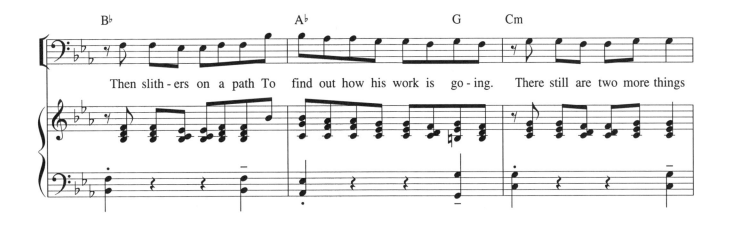

Then slith - ers on a path To find out how his work is go - ing. There still are two more things

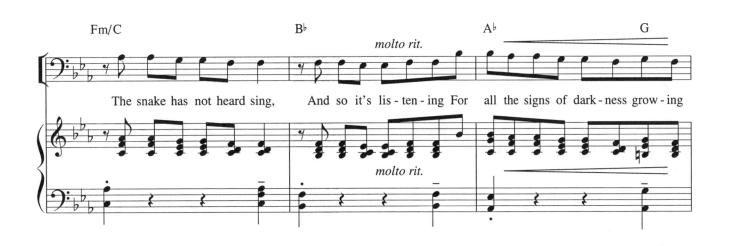

The snake has not heard sing, And so it's lis - ten - ing For all the signs of dark - ness grow - ing

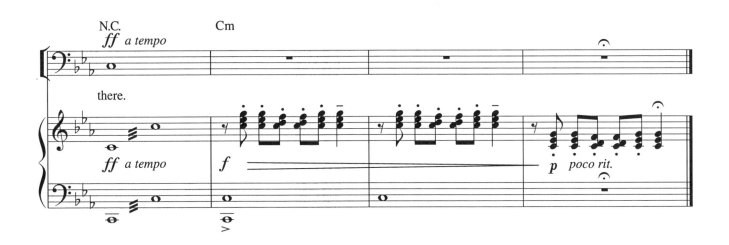

there.

25

There is in the Garden a Barren Tree. Forlorn, the discouraged tree asks, "My branches ache to hold the fruit
I should be bearing… What good will I ever be?"

WHAT GOOD WILL I EVER BE?
(The Barren Tree)

Arranged by
GREG HANSEN

Words and Music by
BRYCE NEUBERT &
MICHAEL McLEAN

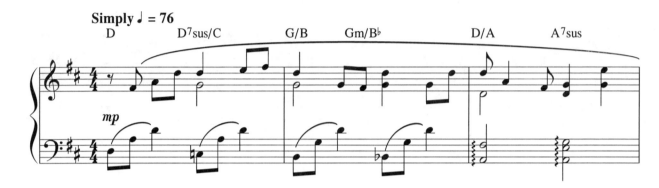

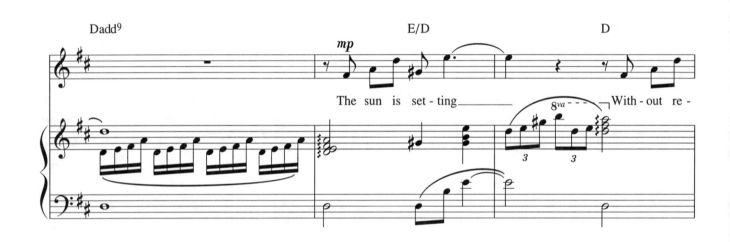

The sun is set-ting_____ With-out re-

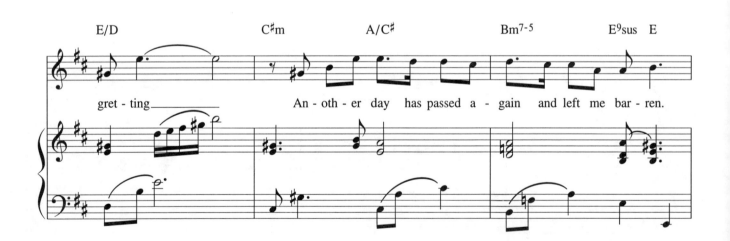

gret-ting_____ An-oth-er day has passed a - gain and left me bar-ren.

Noth - ing is show - ing, No buds are grow - ing; My branch - es ache to hold the fruit I should be bear - ing. And all to - mor - row brings Is mem - o - ries of emp - ty springs. Oh, what good will I ev - er be, A bar - ren and old ol - ive tree?

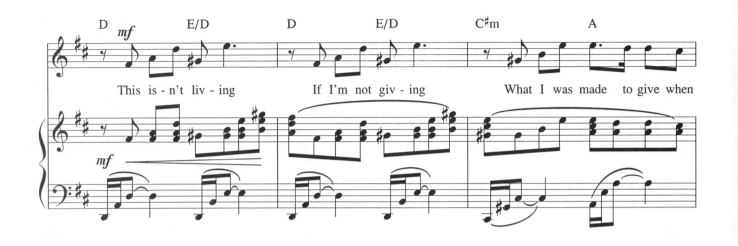

This is-n't liv - ing If I'm not giv - ing What I was made to give when

first I was plant - ed. What curse for - bade me? I'm not a shade tree;

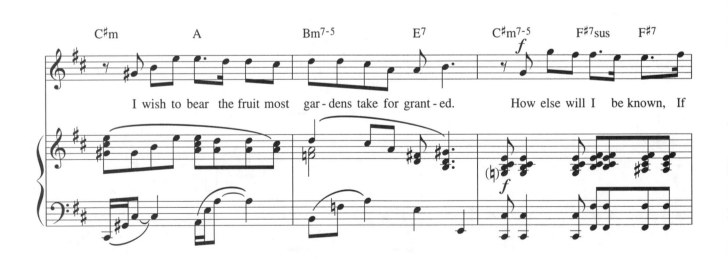

I wish to bear the fruit most gar - dens take for grant - ed. How else will I be known, If

it's not by my fruits a-lone? Oh, what good will I ev - er be, A

bar - ren and old ol - ive tree? This

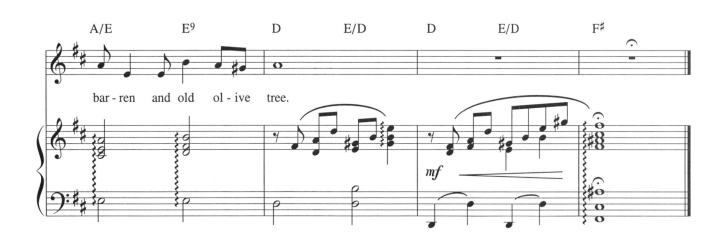

bar - ren and old ol - ive tree.

29

A Millstone struggles with its growing emptiness and despair. Unable to feel anything but hopelessness, it complains, "I feel nothing… Dead as the things I'm crushing… There is no beauty inside me that one could embrace."

I FEEL NOTHING
(The Millstone)

Arranged by
GREG HANSEN

Words and Music by
BRYCE NEUBERT &
MICHAEL McLEAN

Once I had feel - ings in - side of me, now noth - ing's there.

Why should I think that there ought to be an - y - thing there?

I feel noth - ing... Dead as the things I am crush - ing,

I feel noth - ing. Though I faint - ly re - call be - fore I felt

some - thing, but not an - y - more.

Off in the pal - ace a sta - tue is stand - ing, Carved out of mar - ble, com - plete - ly com - mand - ing.

33

Ev - ery - one paus - es to feast on its beau - ty and grace._____

Why could - n't I have been carved, so I'd fit in that place?_____

There is no beau - ty in - side me that one could em - brace._____

I feel noth - ing... Dead as the things I am crush - ing,

34

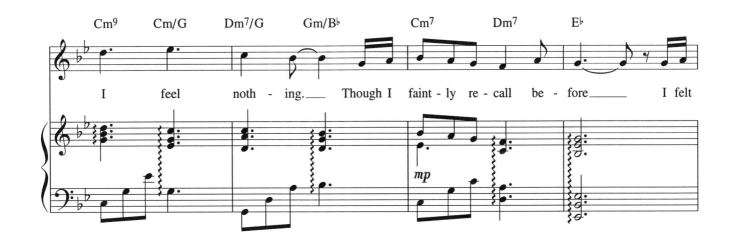

I feel noth - ing.___ Though I faint - ly re - call be - fore___ I felt

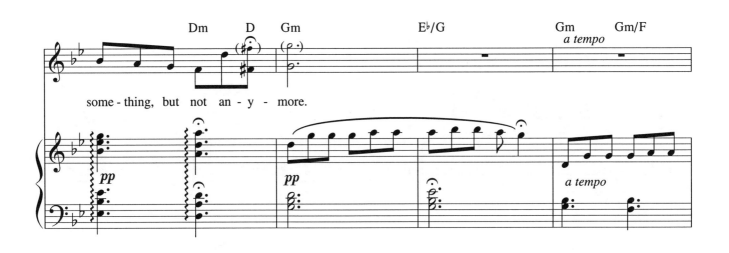

some - thing, but not an - y - more.

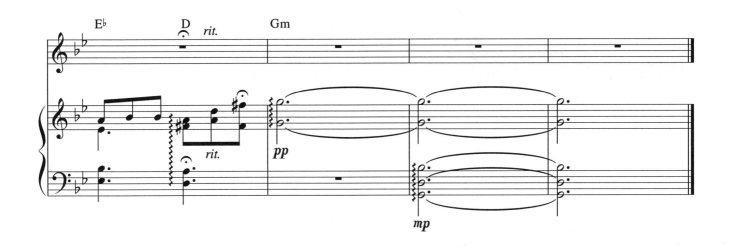

35

Delighted with the depressed, hopeless, and empty feeling that prevails in the Garden, the Snake, the weeds, and the thistles stage a victory celebration of sorts. Things in the Garden are just as they prefer them.

A SNAKE LIES IN THE GRASS/PART 2
(The Chorus)

Arranged by
DAN WALDIS

Words and Music by
BRYCE NEUBERT &
MICHAEL McLEAN

38

39

job that keeps the dark-ness grow-ing. This-tles and weeds are gloat-ing;

Just like the snake, they're know-ing Their choke hold's sure-ly grow-ing

Strong-er. Ev-ery day it's strong-er. The au-thor of this sad-ness,

41

A sweet and noble Gardener introduces a spirit of hopefulness into the Garden. His strong presence helps dissipate the fear and depression that has prevailed. The clouds of despair seem to be clearing.

I HELP THINGS GROW
(The Gardener)

Arranged by
GREG HANSEN

Words and Music by
BRYCE NEUBERT &
MICHAEL McLEAN

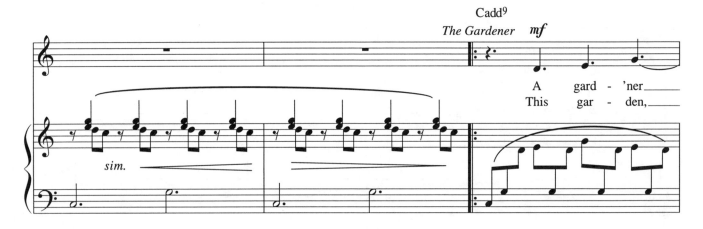

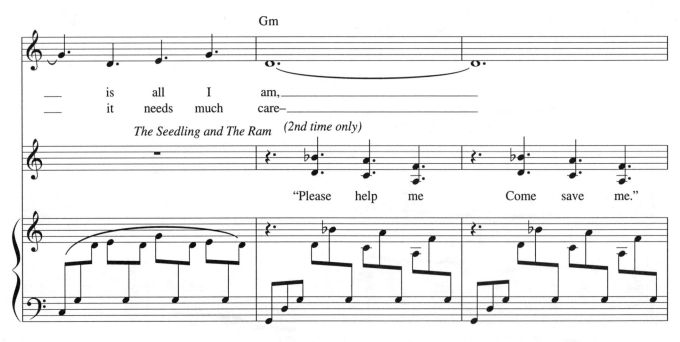

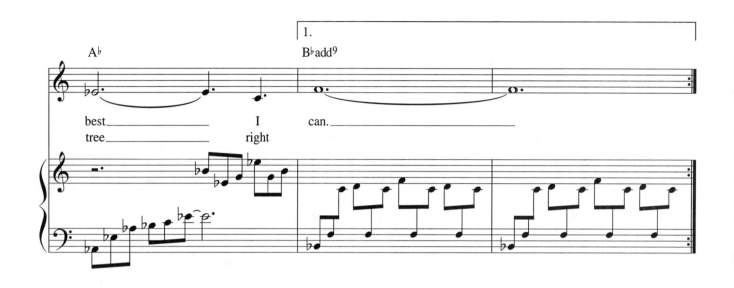

best_____ I can._____
tree_____ right

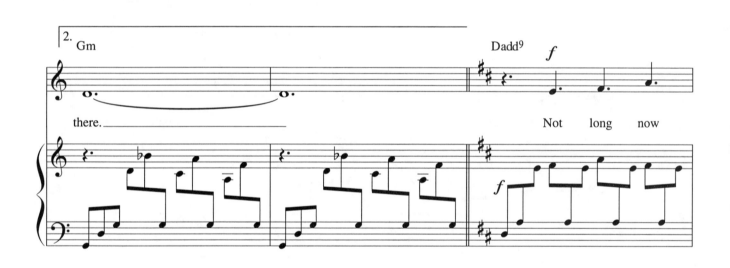

there._____
Not long now

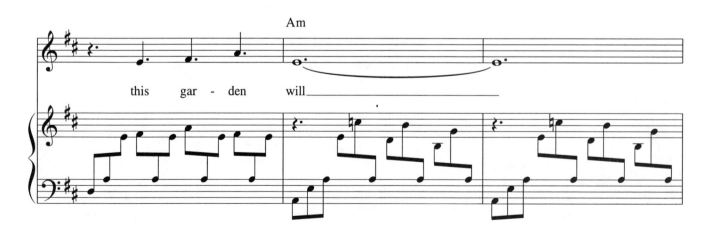

this gar - den will_____

44

segue to "This is My Garden"

Resentful of the Gardener and alarmed by the unexpected turn toward the light, the Landlord, a being very much like the one cast out of our heavenly home, comes to assert his domination of the elements of the Garden: "I am the Landlord here; I've owned this place for years… I thought I made it clear, I want you out of here."

THIS IS MY GARDEN
(The Landlord/The Gardener)

Arranged by
DAN WALDIS

Words and Music by
BRYCE NEUBERT &
MICHAEL McLEAN

48

49

take my place as ov-er-seer. It's best that you just quiet-ly dis-ap - pear.

What be-comes of all that's liv-ing here?_____

You... think you own it. How could you think you

own this gar - den that I love so

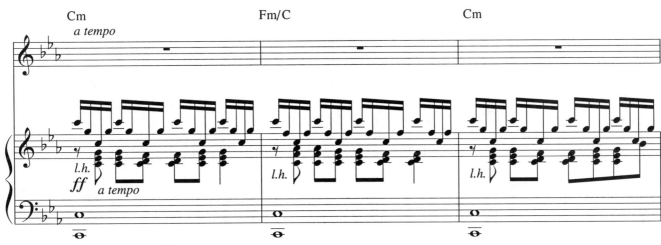

Will o-bey me; I'm their mas-ter. You'll work to re-ar-range it, But you will nev-er change it.

done._____ I won't leave

You'll waste your life to serve it; Noth-ing in this place is worth it. Go a-way!

in fear._____

You know you can't save this gar - den, an - y - way. It's mine to -

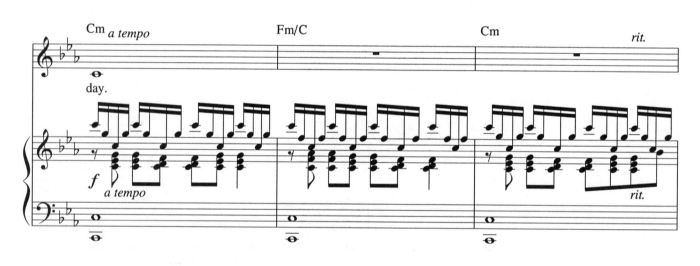

day.

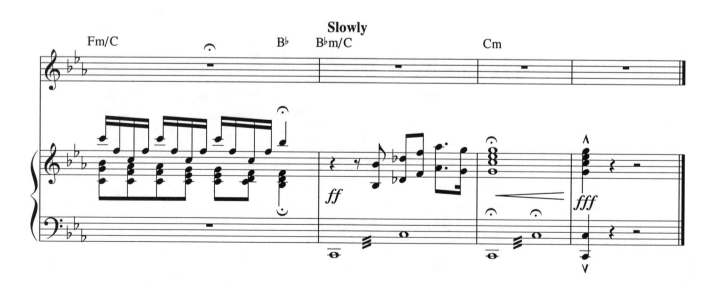

56

Laughing arrogantly, the Landlord leaves the Garden. The bewildered, frightened elements of the Garden approach the kindly Gardener, seeking from him comfort and relief. "Oh, Gardener, please tell us true. If you can't save us, then who?"

I CANNOT SAVE YOU
(The Gardener and the Garden: Seedling, Ram, Tree, and Millstone)

Arranged by
GREG HANSEN

Words and Music by
BRYCE NEUBERT &
MICHAEL McLEAN

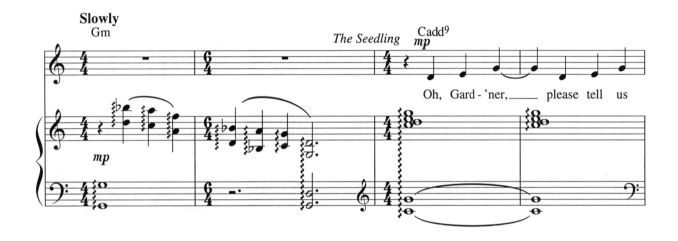

The Tree and Millstone

who?_____ Were that man's words the truth we heard? If so, what will we do?_____

All

Gardener
I can-not save you, it's true,_____ Don't tell us you'll fail us.

58

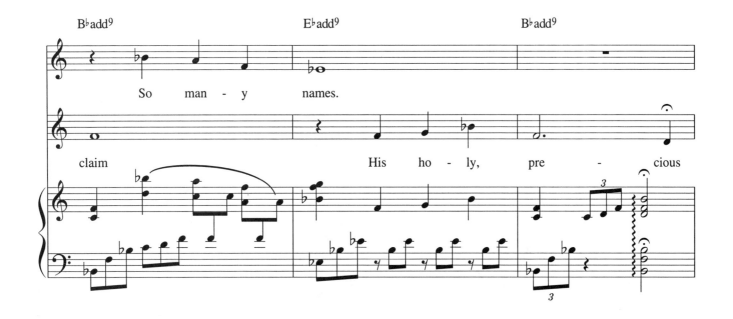

So man - y names.

claim His ho - ly, pre - cious

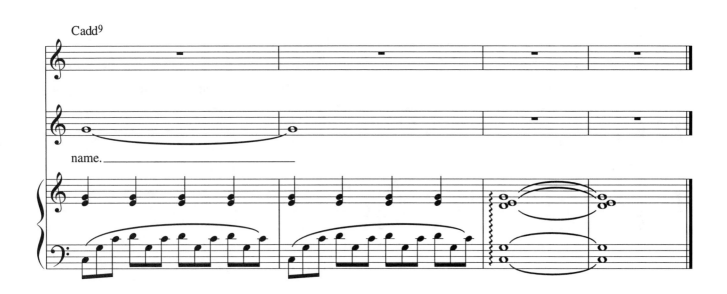

name.

The Gardener cannot save them, but he testifies of One who can–The Man with Many Names. "There is One who to this garden comes, like a most unusual rain–Drink it in and never thirst again."

THE MAN WITH MANY NAMES
(The Gardener)

Arranged by
GREG HANSEN

Words and Music by
BRYCE NEUBERT &
MICHAEL McLEAN

As a hymn ♩ = 76

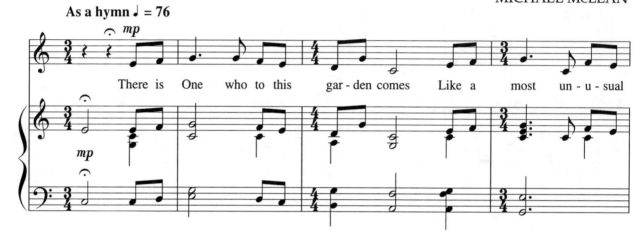

There is One who to this gar-den comes Like a most un-u-sual

rain– Drink it in and nev-er thirst a-gain; Liv-ing Wat-er is___ His

name. There is One who comes to find each one Who has lost his way a-

gain. He will lead the way back to the fold; The Good Shep-herd is_____ His

name. There is One who, when your cry-ing's done, Gives the gifts you've nev - er

known. He'll give fruit be - cause He is The Vine And Life, for He's The Liv - ing

Stone. He is known by, oh, so man - y names, And will be for - ev - er-

more. Hope comes from the One with man - y names, And He's not for - got - ten

yours. No, He's not for - got - ten yours.

The Prophet/Gardener leaves the garden, but a comforting spirit of peace lingers after he is gone. As evening approaches, a heavenly chorus bears a special witness of the saving power of the Man with Many Names. "If we'll just believe, we can receive the healing breath of spring from the One who breathes the hope we need."

THE BREATH OF SPRING
(The Chorus)

Arranged by
GREG HANSEN

Words and Music by
BRYCE NEUBERT &
MICHAEL McLEAN

dawn   of hope is like the   breath of spring–   It   stays   a-while, then__ leaves._____ All too

soon   we   let   our   hearts   for-get   The   joy__ we__ just   re - ceived._____

The

67

68

69

Oo_____ In - to ev - 'ry breath of

From One who breathes the hope we need In - to ev - 'ry breath of

Oo_____ In - to ev - 'ry breath of

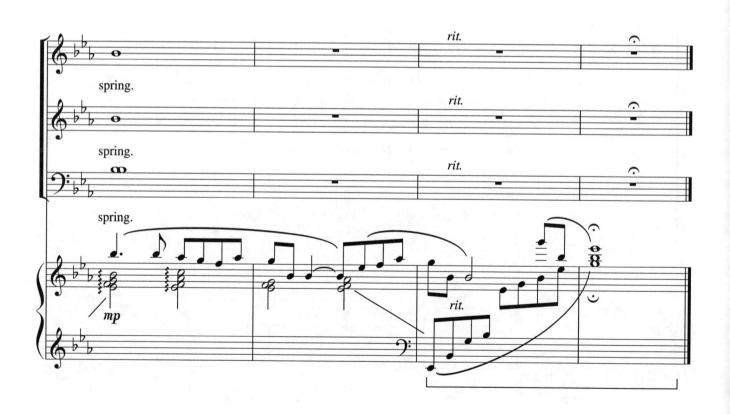

spring.

spring.

spring.

mp

70

It is evening and all is peaceful and quiet. A Man enters the Garden, one who has not been there before. There is nothing imposing about him, but still he stirs the elements, who wonder, "What is this burden he is feeling? It must be heavy, for he's kneeling and struggling to say a prayer."

WHO IS THIS MAN?
(The Seedling, Ram, Tree, and Millstone)

Arranged by
GREG HANSEN

Words and Music by
BRYCE NEUBERT &
MICHAEL McLEAN

Tree: Who is this man who comes to our ter-rain? Per-haps this is the Man with
Seedling: Some-thing a-bout Him, though, seems rath-er frail. His bod-y's strong, and yet his

Man-y Names. *Ram:* Oh, do you think it could be? Dare we be-lieve it would be?
face looks pale. *Millstone:* And, look, as he comes near-er, Could this be our de-liv-'rer,

The Gard-'ner said He'd come and   life would change.   *All:* He's not at all what I im-
This man who's clear-ly filled with such tra - vail?

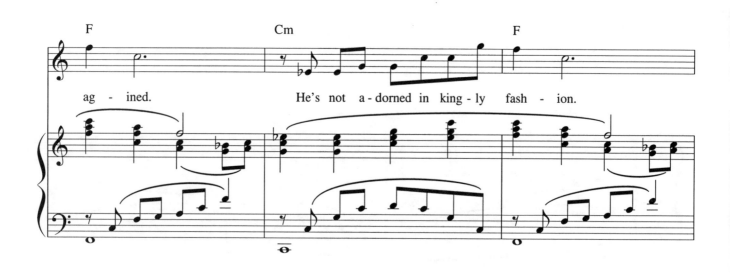

ag - ined.   He's not a-dorned in king-ly fash - ion.

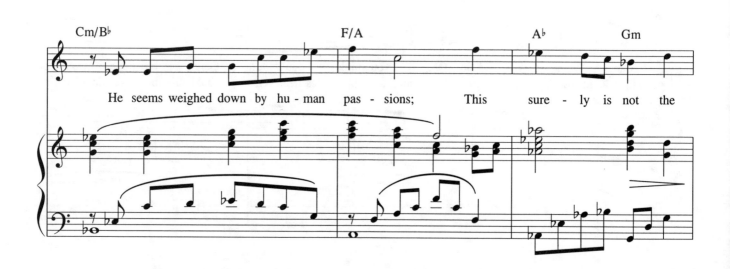

He seems weighed down by hu-man pas - sions;   This   sure - ly is not the

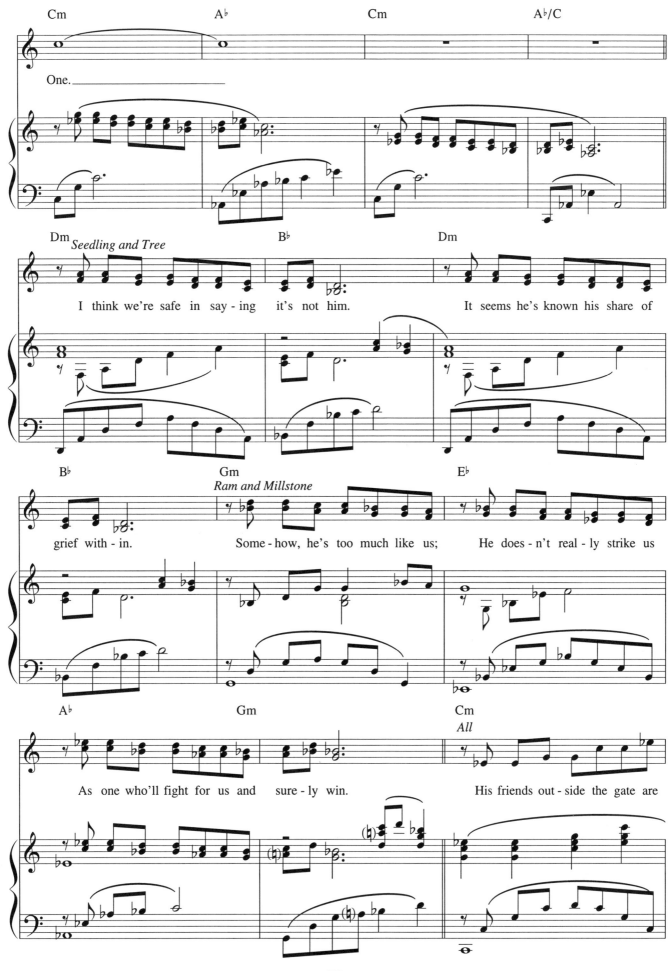

One.

Seedling and Tree

I think we're safe in say-ing it's not him. It seems he's known his share of

grief with-in. *Ram and Millstone* Some-how, he's too much like us; He does-n't real-ly strike us

All As one who'll fight for us and sure-ly win. His friends out-side the gate are

73

sleep - ing.   What is this bur - den he is feel - ing?

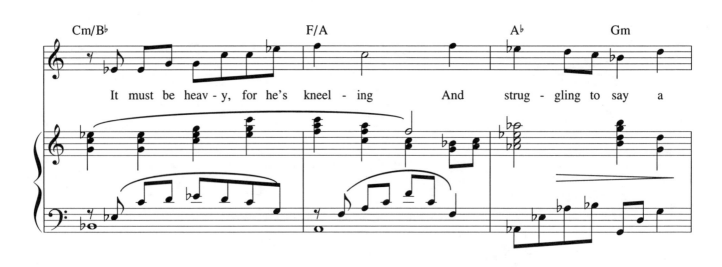

It must be heav - y, for he's kneel - ing   And   strug - gling to say a

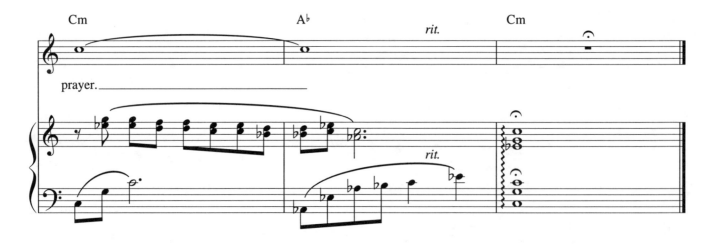

prayer. _____

74

Filled with anguish, this Man of Many Names pours out his heart to God: "Father, let this cup pass from me, but if not,
I will obey." The elements of the Garden marvel at His struggle, while the Landlord ridicules His plight.
It is something the Man must bear alone.

NOT MY WILL

(The Man, Tree, Ram, Millstone, Seedling, Landlord, Gardener, and Chorus)

Arranged by
DAN WALDIS

Words and Music by
BRYCE NEUBERT &
MICHAEL McLEAN

75

76

77

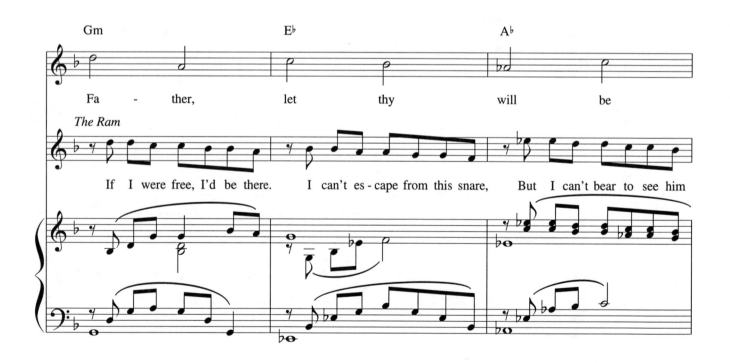

78

79

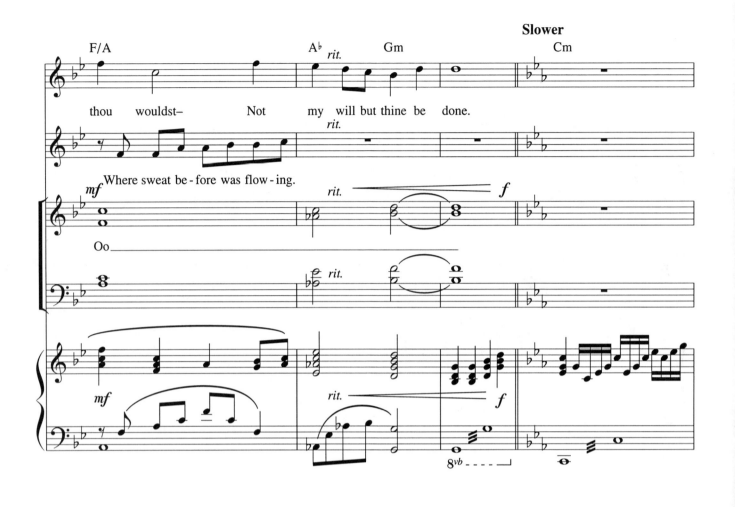

thou wouldst– Not my will but thine be done.

Where sweat be - fore was flow - ing.

Oo

Ah_____ Oo_____ Oo_____

80

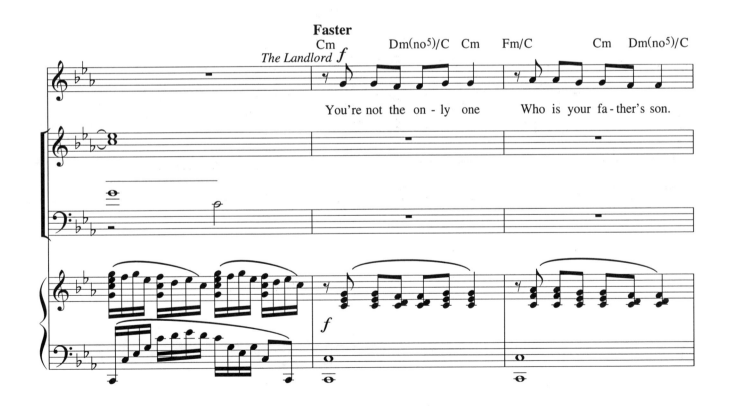

81

This will not work, how dare you? I'm the on - ly lord who's mas - ter here.

All
His pain is flow - ing like a riv - er. Why does - n't he get up and

Chorus
His pain is flow - ing like a riv - er. Why does - n't he get up and

83

leave here?   He's sweat-ing blood and shed-ding more tears—   Oh,

leave here?   He's sweat-ing blood and shed-ding more tears—   Oh,

why must he suf - fer   so?

why must he suf - fer   so?

85

Could show his full sub-mis-sion to such pain.   I can-not look, I have to

Oo_____

turn a-way–   I want to help some-how, but there's no way.

Oo_____

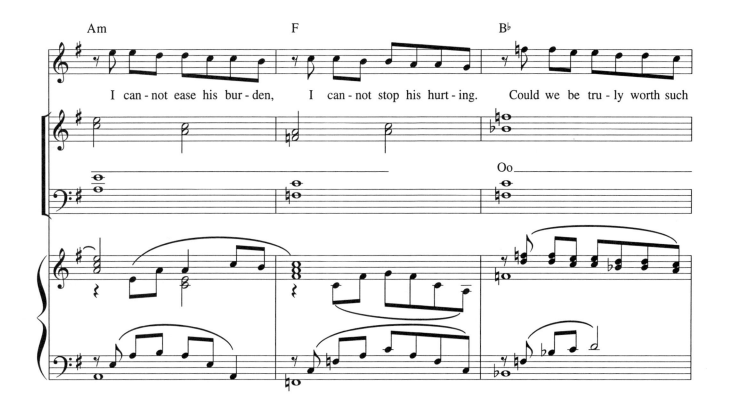

I can - not ease his bur - den, I can - not stop his hurt - ing. Could we be tru - ly worth such

Oo

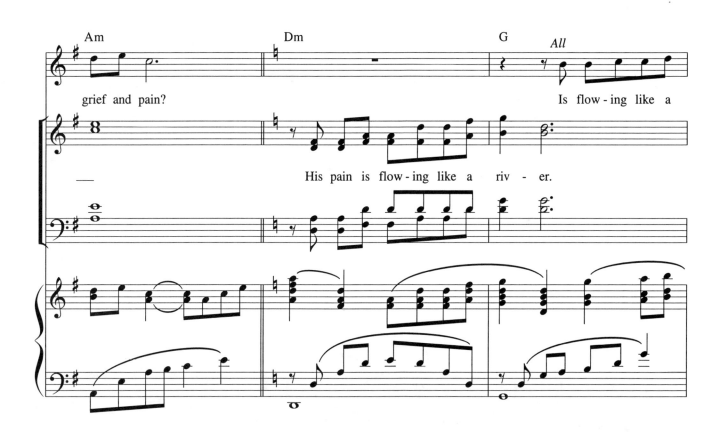

grief and pain?

Is flow - ing like a

His pain is flow - ing like a riv - er.

All

88

The Gardener

90

91

stop the hurt-ing. Could we be tru-ly worth such grief and pain?

This will not work, how dare you? I'm the on - ly lord who's mas-ter here.

Chorus

will be done.

His pain is flow-ing like a

Chorus

But I can't bear to see him suf-fer so.

The Man

I nev - er un - der - stood such an - guish,

But I'm not here to do as

riv - er.

Why does - n't he get up and leave here?

92

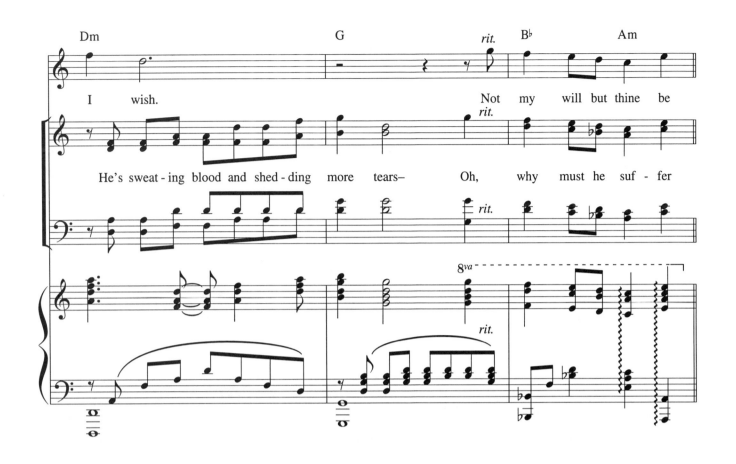

I wish. Not my will but thine be

He's sweat-ing blood and shed-ding more tears— Oh, why must he suf-fer

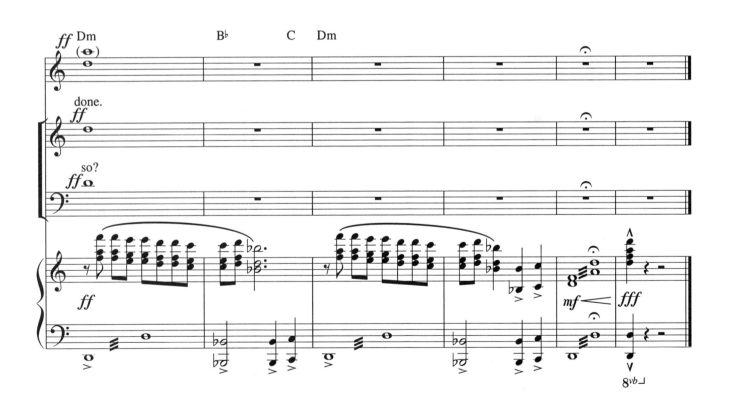

done.

so?

His suffering has been painful to watch, but when it is finished the elements are deeply moved. They have observed a marvelous demonstration of love and sacrifice. Left alone, they fall prey once again to doubt and fear, but then, on the morning of the third day, a new light enters the garden on the hill, and the elements rejoice. Each has been freed and is filled with hope and love–the recipients of the gift from the Man with Many Names.

THE MAN WITH MANY NAMES
(Reprise)

Arranged by
GREG HANSEN

Words and Music by
BRYCE NEUBERT &
MICHAEL McLEAN

What is this that I am feel-ing now? There is sun - light all a-round. Part of me is sway-ing in the breeze; I have grown up from the ground. I am free some-how. I've been set free. It's a mir - a - cle, I'm sure. Where's the

The Tree

One who this great thing has done? I will love Him ev - er - more. Look at

me, this old and bar - ren tree. Not so bar - ren an - y - more; So much

The Millstone

fruit is sweet - ly bud - ding now I could nev - er ask for more. I can

feel some-thing in - side that's real, Like a bright and hope-ful morn. Out of

The Chorus and
the Gardener

death has come a brand new life– I'm a - live... I've been re - born! There is

One who is the on - ly one With the power to bring us home. Rev - 'rent-

ly,   with ev - 'ry   breath we breathe___ We put our   faith in Him   a - lone.   He is

known   by, oh, so   man - y names   And will   be   for - ev - er - more;   Hope comes

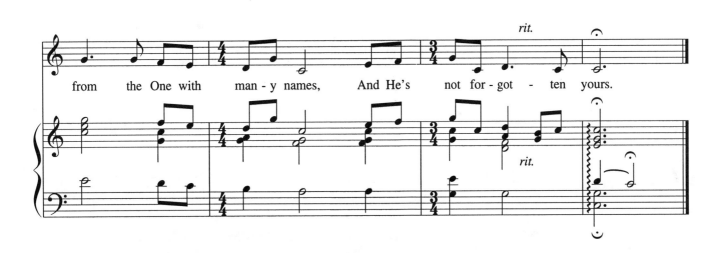

from   the One with   man - y names,   And He's   not for - got - ten   yours.

The soloists and chorus step out of character and now bear joyous testimony of the goodness of the Savior. They sing of having received "the greatest gift of love that ever will be shared." And they finally declare: "He is Jesus Christ. He is come to save us all." It took place "in a garden on a hill, early in the spring."

EPILOGUE

Arranged by
GREG HANSEN

Words and Music by
BRYCE NEUBERT &
MICHAEL McLEAN

all will be___ for - got - ten When we're out there on___ our own, There's a

chance this sto - ry told this hour Will ech - o in our bones In the

mo - ment we most need it– When we're search - ing for what's true– And we

try to com - pre - hend the love He of - fers me and you Who have

As the piece is completed, there is no thunderous applause–no standing ovation–no bouquets of roses for the performers. There is only a feeling of gratitude, peace, and love…and the hope that when we're living in our particular earthly gardens and we're struggling to grow, or when we feel empty or lost or frightened or barren, and we're dangerously close to surrendering to the powers of darkness and despair…that in that very hour something will echo in our bones, something that feels like the breath of spring.

"For the Lord shall comfort Zion: he will comfort all her waste places; and he will make her wilderness like Eden, and her desert like THE GARDEN of the Lord; joy and gladness shall be found therein, thanksgiving, and the voice of melody."

(Isaiah 51:3; emphasis added)